3 Write the key signature and tonic triad of each of the following keys.

Ab major

F♯ minor

E major

B minor

4 Add the correct rest(s) at the places marked * to make each bar complete.

Britten

5 (a) Add the correct clef and any necessary sharp or flat signs to make the scale of F harmonic minor. Do *not* use a key signature.

(b) Write as semibreves (whole notes) the scale of A major, descending, with key signature.

F3

6 Rewrite this melody using notes and a rest of *twice the value*. Remember to put in the new time signature at the place marked *.

Mendelssohn

7 Describe each of these harmonic intervals, giving the type and number (e.g. minor 2nd, perfect 5th). The key is B♭ major.

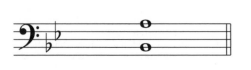 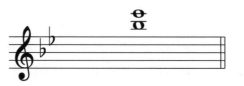 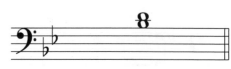

Type ....   Type ....   Type ....

Number ....   Number ....   Number ....

Type ....   Type ....

Number ....   Number ....

Theory of Music Exams

GRADE 3

2010

Theory Paper Grade 3   2010   A

TOTAL MARKS
100

Duration 1½ hours

Candidates should answer ALL questions.
Write your answers on this paper – no others will be accepted.
Answers must be written clearly and neatly – otherwise marks may be lost.

1 Add the time signature to each of these five melodies.

10

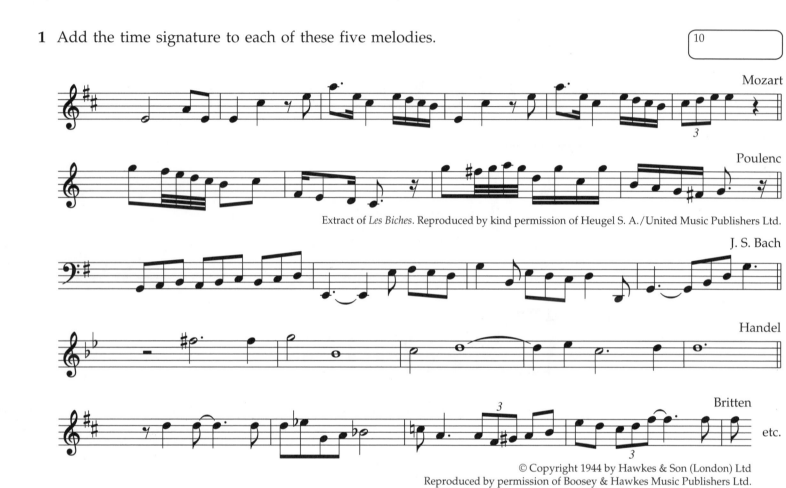

Mozart

Poulenc

Extract of Les Biches. Reproduced by kind permission of Heugel S. A./United Music Publishers Ltd.

J. S. Bach

Handel

Britten

etc.

© Copyright 1944 by Hawkes & Son (London) Ltd
Reproduced by permission of Boosey & Hawkes Music Publishers Ltd.

2 Write a complete four-bar rhythm in $\frac{4}{4}$ time using the given opening.
Remember to complete the first whole bar.

10

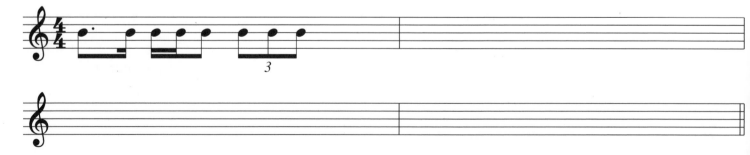

8 Look at this melody by Beethoven and then answer the questions below.

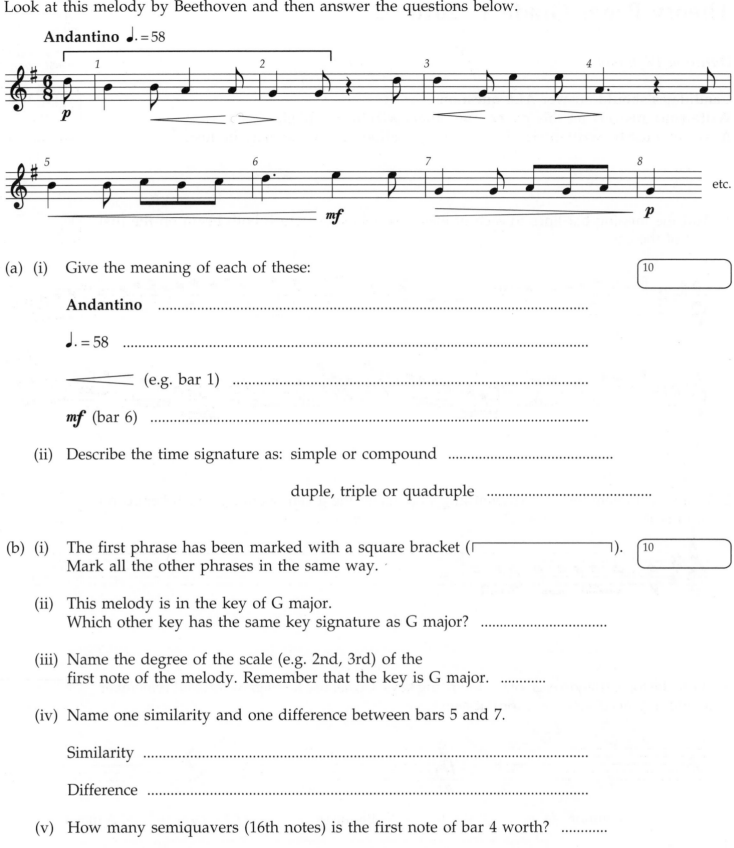

(a) (i) Give the meaning of each of these: [10]

Andantino ....

♩. = 58 ....

⟨ (e.g. bar 1) ....

mf (bar 6) ....

(ii) Describe the time signature as: simple or compound ....

duple, triple or quadruple ....

(b) (i) The first phrase has been marked with a square bracket (⌐⎯⎯⎯⎯¬). [10]
Mark all the other phrases in the same way.

(ii) This melody is in the key of G major.
Which other key has the same key signature as G major? ....

(iii) Name the degree of the scale (e.g. 2nd, 3rd) of the
first note of the melody. Remember that the key is G major. ....

(iv) Name one similarity and one difference between bars 5 and 7.

Similarity ....

Difference ....

(v) How many semiquavers (16th notes) is the first note of bar 4 worth? ....

(c) Write out the melody from the beginning of the music to the first note of bar 4 [10]
an octave lower, using the bass clef as shown.

Theory Paper Grade 3   2010   B

Duration 1½ hours

TOTAL MARKS
100

Candidates should answer ALL questions.
Write your answers on this paper – no others will be accepted.
Answers must be written clearly and neatly – otherwise marks may be lost.

1   Add the missing bar-lines to each of these *two* melodies, which both begin on the first beat of the bar.   `10`

Corelli

J. H. Hasse

2   Write a complete four-bar rhythm in ¾ time using the given opening, which begins on an upbeat.   `10`

3   Write the tonic triad in each of the following keys. Do *not* use key signatures, but remember to add any necessary sharp or flat signs.   `10`

F minor

B♭ major

A major

F♯ minor

E major

6

4 (a) Write as semibreves (whole notes) the scale of C♯ harmonic minor, ascending, with key signature. [10]

(b) Add the correct clef and any necessary sharp or flat signs to make the scale of A♭ major. Do *not* use a key signature.

5 (a) Rewrite the following melody with the notes correctly grouped (beamed). [10]

J. S. Bach

(b) Give the letter name of the note marked ✻ in the final bar. ....

6 This melody by Mozart contains *five* deliberate mistakes. Rewrite it correctly on the given stave. [10]

7 *After* each of these notes write a higher note to form the named *melodic* interval. The key is B minor. [10]

minor 6th

perfect 4th

major 7th

minor 3rd

major 2nd

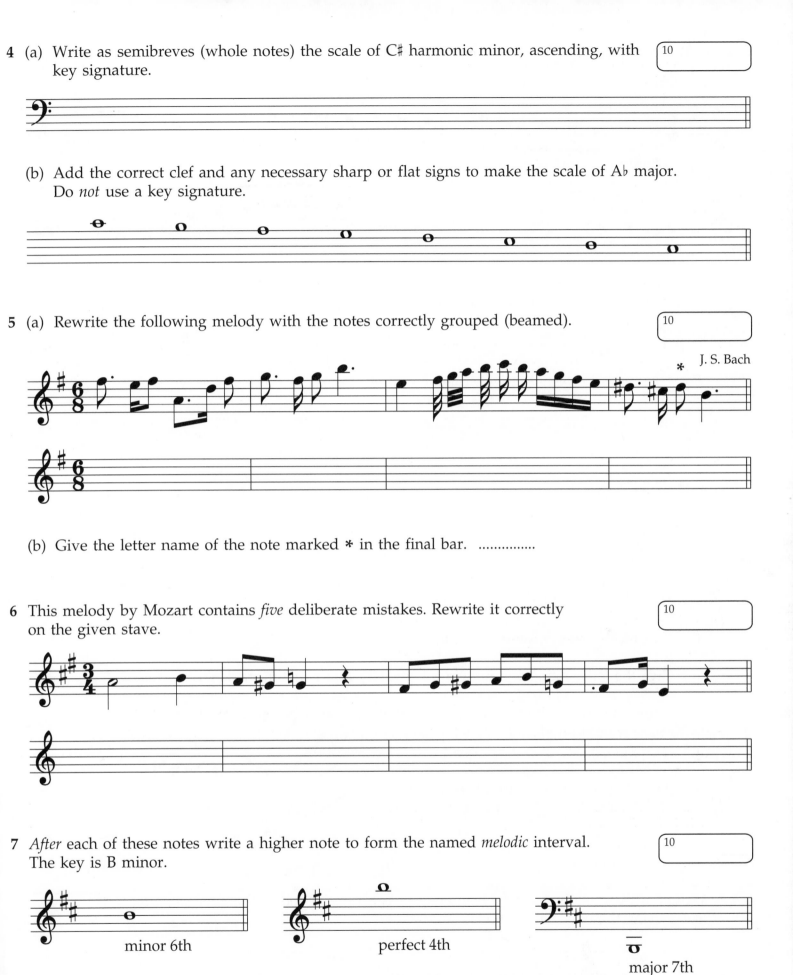

7

8 Look at this melody by Weber and then answer the questions below.

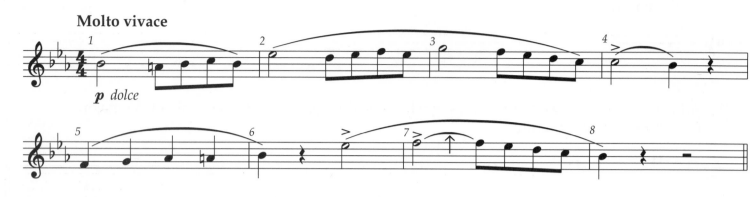

(a) Give the meaning of each of these:

      vivace ....

      p ....

      dolce ....

      > (e.g. bar 4) ....

      ⌢ (bar 7, marked ↑) ....

10

(b) (i) This melody is in the key of E♭ major. Draw a circle around a note which is the 3rd degree of this scale.

      (ii) Which other key has the same key signature as E♭ major? ....

      (iii) Give the letter name of a note in this melody that is *not* in the key of E♭ major. ....

      (iv) Underline one of the following words that best describes how you think this music should be played:

                     legato   *staccato*

      (v) Answer TRUE or FALSE to this statement:
           The rhythm ♩ ♫♫ appears three times. ....

10

(c) Write out the melody from the beginning of bar 5 to the end of the music *an octave lower*, using the bass clef as shown.

10

8

Theory Paper Grade 3   2010   C

Duration 1½ hours

TOTAL MARKS
100

Candidates should answer ALL questions.
Write your answers on this paper – no others will be accepted.
Answers must be written clearly and neatly – otherwise marks may be lost.

1 Add the time signature to each of these five melodies.

10

J. S. Bach

etc.

Britten

Handel

Berlioz

Corelli

2 Write a complete four-bar rhythm in $\frac{9}{8}$ time using the given opening, which begins on
an upbeat.

10

3 This melody by Arne contains *five* deliberate mistakes. Rewrite it correctly
on the given stave.

4 *After* each of these notes write a higher note to form the named *melodic* interval.
The key is E♭ major.

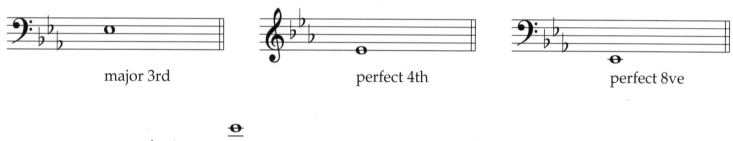

major 3rd   perfect 4th   perfect 8ve

major 2nd   major 7th

5 Add the correct rest(s) at the places marked ✳ to make each bar complete.

Rossini

J. S. Bach

6 (a) Using semibreves (whole notes), write one octave descending of the harmonic minor scale that has the given key signature. Remember to include any necessary sharp or flat signs.

10

(b) Write as semibreves (whole notes) the scale of E major, ascending, without key signature but including any necessary sharp or flat signs.

7 Add the correct clef and key signature to each of these tonic triads.

10

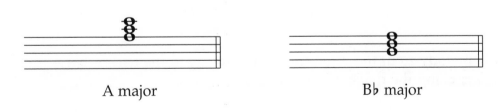

D major   G minor

F♯ minor

A major   B♭ major

11

8 Look at this melody by Elgar and then answer the questions below.

(a) Give the meaning of each of these: [10]

Moderato ....

sostenuto ....

⋀ (e.g. bar 3) ....

dim. (e.g. bar 4) ....

⌣ (bars 6–7, marked ↑) ....

(b) (i) How many times does the rhythm ♩ ♫ ♩ ♩ occur? .... [10]

   (ii) Answer TRUE or FALSE to the following statements:

   The lower **4** in **4/4** means quaver (eighth-note) beats. ....

   Crotchets (quarter notes) and quavers (eighth notes) are the only time values used in bars 1–5 of this melody. ....

   (iii) This melody is in the key of C minor. Name the degree of the scale (e.g. 4th, 5th) of the first note of the melody. ....

   (iv) Draw a circle around the note which you think will sound the *quietest*.

(c) Write out the melody from the beginning of the music to the end of bar 4 *an octave higher,* using the treble clef as shown. [10]

Theory Paper Grade 3   2010   S

Duration 1½ hours

TOTAL MARKS
100

Candidates should answer ALL questions.
Write your answers on this paper – no others will be accepted.
Answers must be written clearly and neatly – otherwise marks may be lost.

1 (a) Add the missing bar-lines to each of these *two* melodies, which both begin on the first beat of the bar.

10

(b) Describe the time signature of $\frac{12}{8}$ as: simple or compound ....

duple, triple or quadruple ....

2 Write a complete four-bar rhythm in $\frac{4}{2}$ time using the given opening, which begins on an upbeat.

10

3 Add the correct clef and any necessary sharp or flat signs to each of these tonic triads. Do *not* use key signatures.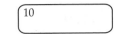

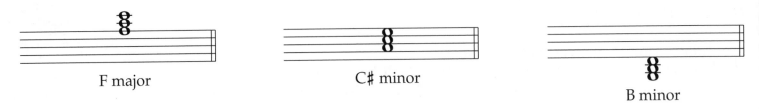

F major   C♯ minor   B minor

D major   A♭ major

4 Transpose this melody *up* an octave, using the treble clef as shown. [10]

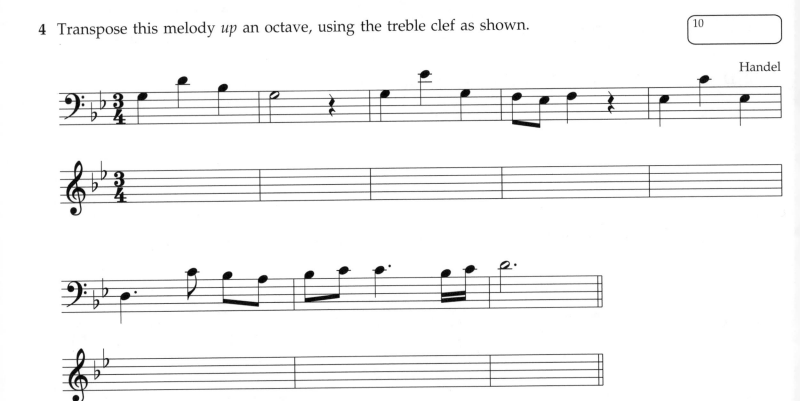

Handel

5 Describe each of these melodic intervals, giving the type and number (e.g. major 2nd, perfect 4th). The keys are named, and in each case the lower note is the key note. [10]

Bb major

Type ....

Number ....

C minor

Type ....

Number ....

E major

Type ....

Number ....

F# minor

Type ....

Number ....

A minor

Type ....

Number ....

6 Write as semibreves (whole notes) the scales named below. [10]

Eb major, descending, without key signature but including any necessary sharp or flat signs

B melodic minor, ascending, with key signature

7 This melody contains *five* deliberate mistakes. Rewrite it correctly on the given stave. [10]

Sullivan

8 Look at this melody by Schubert and then answer the questions below.

(a) Give the meaning of each of these:

Andante ....

the lower **2** in **2/2** ....

p ....

⌣ (e.g. bar 2) ....

⸺ (e.g. bar 3) ....

(b) (i) Complete this statement:
   Bar 3 has the same rhythm as bar ....

   (ii) This melody is in the key of A♭ major. Give the number
   of a bar that contains a note which is *not* in this key. Bar ....

   (iii) Name the degree of the scale (e.g. 3rd, 4th) of the
   first note of bar 6. Remember that the key is A♭ major. ....

   (iv) Which other key has the same key signature as A♭ major? ....

   (v) How many semiquavers (16th notes) is the first note of bar 4 worth? ....

(c) Write out the melody from the beginning of the music to the third note of bar 4
   using notes of *half the value*. Remember to put in the new time signature at the
   place marked ✳.

ABRSM
24 Portland Place
London W1B 1LU
United Kingdom

www.abrsm.org

Theory of Music Exams Model Answers
are also available.

Published by ABRSM (Publishing) Ltd,
a wholly owned subsidiary of ABRSM

Printed in England by Page Bros (Norwich) Ltd
10/10

9781848492882
WT
02/11
E   £2.95

ISBN 978-1-84849-288-